Physics for the Grammar Stage

Student Workbook

Physics for the Grammar Stage Student Workbook

Third Edition (First Printing 2021)
Copyright @ Elemental Science, Inc.
Email: support@elementalscience.com

ISBN# 978-1-953490-13-1

Printed in the USA for worldwide distribution

For more copies write to:
Elemental Science
PO Box 79
Niceville, FL 32588
support@elementalscience.com

Copyright Policy

Classical SCIENCE

A Quick Welcome from the Author

Dear Student,

Welcome to physics! This workbook will serve as a scrapbook of sorts for you to share what you have learned about the principles of physics. You will be learning about forces, motion, energy, and so much more.

Each week you and your teacher will do the following:

- **Read** the assigned pages together. Your teacher will then ask you a few questions as you discuss what was read. Be sure to share what you found interesting.

- **Do** the weekly demonstration with your teacher. This is the super fun part of science, plus you get to exercise your observation muscles. Be sure to pay close attention and help out when your teachers ask you to do so.

- **Write** down what you have learned and seen. Your teacher may help you with the actual writing, but be sure to record the facts that you want to remember.

Your teacher has the tools to add in more each week, things like memory work, library books, and extra activities. Be sure to let them know if you want to dig deeper into a topic.

And, if you have a question or want to share your work with me, please have your teacher send us an email (support@elementalscience.com) or tag us (@elementalscience) in a photo you share online. I would love to see what you have learned!

I hope that you enjoy learning about physics this year!

Paige Hudson

Table of Contents

A Peek Inside Your Student Workbook

1. Weekly Notebooking Pages

Here is your chance to share what you found interesting about what you read about each week. Each of these customized notebooking pages have space for you (or your teacher) to write, along with a simple black-line illustration for you to color.

2. Simple Demonstration Sheets

These pages allow you to document the hands-on scientific demonstrations you do with your teacher. There are sections for your materials, your method, your outcome, and your insights, or thoughts, from the demonstration.

3. Glossary of Terms

You can keep a glossary of words that you covered this year as part of your student workbook. These words are listed in alphabetical order with pictures to help you remember the vocabulary.

4. Memory Worksheets

You can work on the memory work with the poster-style sheets found after the glossary. Each poem has illustrations you can color that will help you remember the information in the poem.

5. Review Sheets

Finally, you will see review sheets at the back of this workbook. These may or may not be assigned by your teacher.

And now that you know what is in your workbook, let's dig in!

Physics for the Grammar Stage Student Workbook ~ At a Glance

Physics for the Grammar Stage

Energy Unit

8

Catapult Diary

Week 1: Simple Marshmallow Catapult

_____

_____

_____

_____

_____

_____

_____

_____

_____

_____

Week 2: My Catapult Design

Week 3 and 4: Building and Testing My Catapult

_____

_____

_____

_____

_____

_____

_____

_____

Week 5: Changes I Would Make

_____

_____

_____

_____

_____

Energy Basics

_____

_____

_____

_____

_____

_____

_____

_____

_____

_____

_____

_____

_____

_____

_____

_____

_____

Law of Conservation of Energy

_____

_____

_____

Demonstration Report: Energy Relocation

Our Tools

_____   _____

_____   _____

Our Method

What it looked like

Our Outcome

Our Insight

Energy Resources

_____

_____

_____

_____

_____

_____

_____

_____

_____

_____

_____

_____

_____

_____

_____

_____

Physics for the Grammar Stage Student Workbook ~ Energy Unit Week 2

Demonstration Report: Wind Energy

Our Tools

_____   _____

_____   _____

Our Method

┌─────────────────────────────┐
│   What it looked like   │   _____
│   │   _____
│   │   _____
│   │   _____
│   │   _____
│   │   _____
│   │   _____
│   │   _____
│   │   _____
└─────────────────────────────┘   _____

Our Outcome

_____

_____

_____

_____

_____

Our Insight

_____

_____

_____

Nuclear Energy

_____
_____
_____
_____
_____
_____
_____
_____
_____
_____
_____
_____
_____
_____
_____
_____

Demonstration Report: Balloon Fission

Our Tools

_____   _____

_____   _____

Our Method

What it looked like

Our Outcome

Our Insight

Heat

_____

_____

_____

_____

_____

_____

_____

_____

_____

_____

_____

Demonstration Report: Hot or Cold

Our Tools

_____   _____

_____   _____

Our Method

_____

_____

_____

_____

_____

Our Outcome

	Left Hand	Right Hand
How it felt in the outside bowl		
How it felt in the middle bowl		

_____

_____

_____

Our Insight

_____

_____

_____

Heat Transfer

_____

_____

_____

_____

_____

_____

_____

_____

_____

_____

_____

_____

_____

_____

_____

_____

_____

_____

Demonstration Report: Water Heater

Our Tools

_____   _____

_____   _____

Our Method

_____

_____

_____

_____

_____

Our Outcome

	At beginning	After 30 minutes	After 60 minutes	After 90 minutes	After 120 minutes
Temperature					

_____

_____

_____

_____

Our Insight

_____

_____

Physics for the Grammar Stage

Light Unit

Light Box Diary

Week 1: Light Play

Week 2: Color Play

Week 3: Water Play

Week 4: Lens and Mirrors Play

Light

_____

_____

_____

_____

_____

_____

_____

_____

_____

_____

_____

_____

_____

Demonstration Report: Sight Box

Our Tools

_____   _____

_____   _____

Our Method

_____

_____

_____

_____

_____

Our Outcome

What I saw the 1st time	What I saw the 2nd time

Our Insight

_____

_____

_____

Colors

_____

_____

_____

_____

_____

_____

_____

_____

_____

_____

_____

_____

_____

_____

_____

_____

Physics for the Grammar Stage Student Workbook ~ Light Unit Week 2

Demonstration Report: Whirling Colors

Our Tools

_____   _____

_____   _____

Our Method

What it looked like

_____
_____
_____
_____
_____
_____
_____
_____

Our Outcome

_____
_____
_____
_____
_____

Our Insight

_____
_____
_____

Light Behavior

_____

_____

_____

_____

_____

_____

_____

_____

_____

_____

_____

_____

_____

_____

_____

_____

Light

Mirror

Light

Lens

Demonstration Report: Refraction Action

Our Tools

_____   _____

_____   _____

Our Method

What it looked like

_____

_____

_____

_____

_____

_____

_____

_____

_____

Our Outcome

_____

_____

_____

_____

Our Insight

_____

_____

_____

Lenses and Mirrors

_____

_____

_____

_____

_____

_____

_____

_____

_____

_____

_____

_____

_____

_____

Demonstration Report: Glass Lens

Our Tools

_____   _____

_____   _____

Our Method

_____

_____

_____

_____

_____

The Message

Our Outcome

_____

Our Insight

_____

_____

_____

Scientist Biography Questionnaire – Thomas Edison

Title of Book

_____

When and where was Thomas Edison born?

_____

_____

What was his major scientific contribution?

_____

_____

_____

_____

_____

List the events that surround his discovery.

_____

_____

_____

_____

_____

_____

_____

_____

_____

_____

_____

_____

List some other interesting events in the his life.

_____

_____

_____

_____

_____

_____

_____

_____

_____

_____

_____

Why do you think that it is important to learn about Thomas Edison?

_____

_____

_____

_____

_____

_____

_____

Physics for the Grammar Stage

Sound Unit

Homemade Sound Diary

Week 1: _____

_____

_____

_____

_____

_____

_____

_____

_____

_____

_____

Week 2: _____

_____

_____

_____

_____

_____

_____

_____

_____

_____

_____

Homemade Sound Diary

Week 3: _____

_____

_____

_____

_____

_____

_____

_____

_____

_____

_____

Week 4: _____

_____

_____

_____

_____

_____

_____

_____

_____

_____

Physics for the Grammar Stage Student Workbook ~ Sound Unit Project

Sound

Physics for the Grammar Stage Student Workbook ~ Sound Unit Week 1

Demonstration Report: Sound Energy

Our Tools

_____   _____

_____   _____

Our Method

+-----------------------------+ _____
| What it looked like | _____
| | _____
| | _____
| | _____
| | _____
| | _____
| | _____
| | _____
+-----------------------------+

Our Outcome

_____

_____

_____

_____

Our Insight

_____

_____

_____

Waves

_____

_____

_____

_____

_____

_____

_____

_____

_____

_____

_____

_____

_____

_____

_____

_____

_____

_____

_____

Demonstration Report: Wave Motion

Our Tools

_____   _____

_____   _____

Our Method

What it looked like

_____
_____
_____
_____
_____
_____
_____
_____
_____

Our Outcome

_____
_____
_____
_____

Our Insight

_____
_____
_____
_____

Wave Behavior

Demonstration Report: Hearing Interference

Our Tools

_____   _____

_____   _____

Our Method

_____

_____

_____

_____

_____

Our Outcome

	Loudness (1 = soft, 10=loud)									
Plain	1	2	3	4	5	6	7	8	9	10
With Cardboard	1	2	3	4	5	6	7	8	9	10
With Cup	1	2	3	4	5	6	7	8	9	10

Our Insight

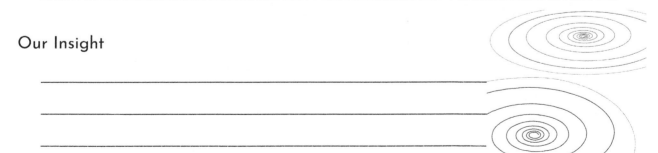

_____

_____

_____

Musical Instruments

_____

_____

_____

_____

_____

_____

_____

_____

_____

_____

_____

_____

_____

_____

Demonstration Report: Rubberband Band

Our Tools

_____   _____

_____   _____

Our Method

What it looked like

_____

_____

_____

_____

_____

_____

_____

_____

Our Outcome

_____

_____

_____

_____

_____

Our Insight

_____

_____

_____

Physics for the Grammar Stage

Electricity Unit

Circuit Project Diary

Week 1: _____

_____

_____

_____

_____

_____

_____

_____

Week 2: _____

_____

_____

_____

_____

_____

_____

_____

Week 3: _____

_____

_____

_____

_____

_____

_____

_____

Circuit Project Diary

Week 4: _____

_____

_____

_____

_____

_____

_____

_____

_____

Week 5: _____

_____

_____

_____

_____

_____

_____

_____

_____

Electricity

_____
_____
_____
_____
_____
_____
_____
_____
_____
_____
_____
_____
_____
_____
_____

Demonstration Report: Invisible Current

Our Tools

_____   _____

_____   _____

Our Method

What it looked like

_____

_____

_____

_____

_____

_____

_____

_____

_____

Our Outcome

_____

_____

_____

_____

_____

Our Insight

_____

_____

_____

Circuits and Batteries

_____
_____
_____
_____
_____
_____
_____
_____
_____
_____
_____
_____
_____
_____
_____

BATTERY +

_____
_____
_____
_____
_____
_____
_____

Demonstration Report: Simple Circuit

Our Tools

_____   _____

_____   _____

Our Method

What it looked like

_____

_____

_____

_____

_____

_____

_____

_____

_____

Our Outcome

_____

_____

_____

_____

Our Insight

_____

_____

_____

Magnets

_____
_____
_____
_____
_____
_____
_____
_____
_____
_____
_____
_____
_____
_____

_____
_____
_____
_____
_____
_____
_____
_____
_____

Demonstration Report: Magnetic Exploration

Our Tools

_____   _____

_____   _____

Our Method

_____

_____

_____

_____

Our Outcome

Testing Material	Was it attracted to the magnet?	
	Yes	No
	Yes	No
	Yes	No
	Yes	No

Our Insight

_____

_____

Electronics

Demonstration Report: Deconstruction

Our Tools

_____   _____

_____   _____

Our Method

_____

_____

_____

Our Outcome

A picture of the inside of my deconstructed electronic

Our Insight

_____

_____

_____

_____

Computers and Coding

Physics for the Grammar Stage

Forces Unit

Egg Drop Carrier Diary

Week 1: Shock-Absorbing Material Testing

Material	Sound level

Week 2: Parachute Materials Testing

Material	Drop Time

Week 3 and 4: Designing and Building My Egg Drop Carrier

Week 5: Testing My Egg Drop Carrier

_____

_____

_____

_____

_____

_____

_____

_____

_____

_____

_____

Forces

_____

_____

_____

_____

_____

_____

_____

_____

_____

_____

_____

_____

_____

_____

_____

_____

_____

_____

_____

_____

_____

_____

_____

Demonstration Report: Force Lab

Our Tools

_____   _____

_____   _____

Our Method

_____

_____

_____

_____

_____

Our Outcome

Test	My Observations
Test #1 (Push)	
Test #2 (Pull)	
Test #3 (Both)	

Our Insight

_____

_____

_____

Balance

_____

_____

_____

_____

_____

_____

_____

_____

_____

_____

_____

_____

_____

_____

_____

_____

_____

_____

_____

_____

Demonstration Report: Balance Tower

Our Tools

_____   _____

_____   _____

Our Method

What it looked like

_____

_____

_____

_____

_____

_____

_____

_____

_____

Our Outcome

_____

_____

_____

_____

_____

Our Insight

_____

_____

_____

Gravity

_____
_____
_____
_____
_____
_____
_____
_____
_____
_____
_____
_____
_____
_____
_____

Demonstration Report: Rolling Pencil

Our Tools

_____   _____

_____   _____

Our Method

_____

_____

_____

_____

_____

Our Outcome

	Flat surface	At an angle	Pushing it up
My Observations			

_____

_____

_____

Our Insight

_____

_____

_____

Friction

_____
_____
_____
_____
_____
_____
_____
_____
_____
_____
_____
_____
_____
_____

                              _____
                              _____
                              _____
                              _____
                              _____
                              _____
                              _____

Demonstration Report: Friction Roll

Our Tools

_____   _____

_____   _____

Our Method

_____

_____

_____

_____

_____

Our Outcome

	Smooth surface	Surface with paper	Surface with felt
Marble Roll Time			

_____

_____

_____

_____

Our Insight

_____

_____

_____

Floating

_____

_____

_____

_____

_____

_____

_____

_____

_____

_____

_____

_____

_____

_____

_____

_____

_____

_____

_____

_____

_____

Demonstration Report: Floating Ship

Our Tools

_____   _____

_____   _____

Our Method

What it looked like

_____
_____
_____
_____
_____
_____
_____
_____

Our Outcome

_____
_____
_____
_____
_____

Our Insight

_____
_____
_____

Physics for the Grammar Stage

Motion Unit

Rocket Diary

Week 1: Building My Rocket

Week 2: Launching My Rocket

_____

_____

_____

Week 3: Improving My Rocket

_____

_____

_____

_____

_____

_____

Dynamics

_____
_____
_____
_____
_____
_____
_____
_____
_____
_____
_____
_____
_____
_____
_____
_____

_____
_____
_____
_____
_____

Demonstration Report: Third Law

Our Tools

_____   _____

_____   _____

Our Method

What it looked like

_____
_____
_____
_____
_____
_____
_____
_____
_____

Our Outcome

_____
_____
_____
_____
_____

Our Insight

_____
_____
_____

Speed

_____
_____
_____
_____
_____
_____
_____
_____
_____
_____
_____
_____
_____

_____
_____
_____
_____
_____
_____
_____
_____

Demonstration Report: Accelerate

Our Tools

_____   _____

_____   _____

Our Method

_____

_____

_____

_____

_____

Our Outcome

Path	Time to Stop
Flat Ground	
Down a Ramp	
Up a Ramp	

_____

_____

_____

Our Insight

_____

_____

_____

Circular Motion

_____

_____

_____

_____

_____

_____

_____

_____

_____

_____

_____

_____

_____

_____

_____

_____

_____

_____

_____

_____

Demonstration Report: Circular Penny

Our Tools

_____   _____

_____   _____

Our Method

+-------------------------+   _____
| What it looked like | _____
| | _____
| | _____
| | _____
| | _____
| | _____
| | _____
| | _____
| | _____
+-------------------------+   _____

Our Outcome

_____

_____

_____

_____

_____

Our Insight

_____

_____

_____

Scientist Biography Questionnaire - Isaac Newton

Title of Book

_____

When and where was Isaac Newton born?

_____

_____

What was his major scientific contribution?

_____

_____

_____

_____

_____

List the events that surround his discovery.

_____

_____

_____

_____

_____

_____

_____

_____

_____

_____

_____

_____

List some other interesting events in the his life.

_____

_____

_____

_____

_____

_____

_____

_____

_____

_____

_____

Why do you think that it is important to learn about Isaac Newton?

_____

_____

_____

_____

_____

_____

_____

Physics for the Grammar Stage

Engineering Unit

Building Projects Diary

Project 1: _____

_____

_____

_____

_____

_____

_____

_____

_____

_____

_____

Project 2: _____

_____

_____

_____

_____

_____

_____

_____

_____

_____

_____

Building Projects Diary

Project 3: _____

_____

_____

_____

_____

_____

_____

_____

_____

_____

Project 4: _____

_____

_____

_____

_____

_____

_____

_____

_____

_____

Building Projects Diary

Project 5: _____

_____

_____

_____

_____

_____

_____

_____

_____

_____

Project 6: _____

_____

_____

_____

_____

_____

_____

_____

_____

_____

Building Projects Diary

Project 7: _____

_____

_____

_____

_____

_____

_____

_____

_____

_____

Ramps, Levers, and Screws

_____

_____

_____

_____

_____

_____

_____

_____

_____

_____

_____

_____

_____

_____

_____

_____

_____

_____

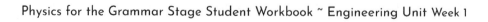

Demonstration Report: Nail versus Screw

Our Tools

_____   _____

_____   _____

Our Method

_____

_____

_____

_____

_____

Our Outcome

	Effort Required (1 = easy, 10 = very difficult)									
Nail through cardboard	1	2	3	4	5	6	7	8	9	10
Pulling cardboard off the nail	1	2	3	4	5	6	7	8	9	10
Screw through cardboard	1	2	3	4	5	6	7	8	9	10
Pulling cardboard off the screw	1	2	3	4	5	6	7	8	9	10

Our Insight

_____

_____

_____

Wheels, Gears, and Pulleys

_____

_____

_____

_____

_____

_____

_____

_____

_____

_____

_____

_____

_____

_____

_____

_____

_____

Demonstration Report: Simple Wheel

Our Tools

_____   _____

_____   _____

Our Method

_____

_____

_____

_____

_____

Our Outcome

	Effort Required (1 = easy, 10 = very difficult)									
Along the surface	1	2	3	4	5	6	7	8	9	10
Along the pencil path	1	2	3	4	5	6	7	8	9	10

_____

_____

_____

Our Insight

_____

_____

_____

_____

Turbines, Pumps, and Hydraulics

_____

_____

_____

_____

_____

_____

_____

_____

_____

_____

_____

_____

_____

_____

_____

_____

_____

_____

Demonstration Report: Hydraulic Push

Our Tools

_____   _____

_____   _____

Our Method

What it looked like

_____

_____

_____

_____

_____

_____

_____

_____

Our Outcome

_____

_____

_____

_____

Our Insight

_____

_____

_____

Engineering

_____

_____

_____

_____

_____

_____

_____

_____

_____

_____

_____

_____

_____

_____

_____

_____

                                        _____

                                        _____

                                        _____

                                        _____

                                        _____

                                        _____

                                        _____

                                        _____

Demonstration Report: LEGO® Balloon Car

Our Tools

_____   _____

_____   _____

Our Method

What it looked like

_____
_____
_____
_____
_____
_____
_____
_____
_____

Our Outcome

_____
_____
_____
_____
_____

Our Insight

_____
_____
_____

98

Building Materials

_____

_____

_____

_____

_____

_____

_____

_____

_____

_____

_____

_____

_____

_____

_____

_____

_____

_____

_____

_____

_____

_____

Demonstration Report: Bioplastic

Our Tools

_____   _____

_____   _____

Our Method

> ### What it looked like

_____
_____
_____
_____
_____
_____
_____
_____
_____

Our Outcome

_____
_____
_____
_____

Our Insight

_____
_____
_____

Bridges and Arches

_____

_____

_____

_____

_____

_____

_____

_____

_____

_____

_____

_____

_____

_____

_____

_____

_____

_____

Demonstration Report: Straw Bridge

Our Tools

_____   _____

_____   _____

Our Method

_____

_____

_____

_____

_____

Our Outcome

Number of pennies the straw bridge could hold

_____

_____

_____

_____

Our Insight

_____

_____

_____

_____

_____

Modern Machines

_____

_____

_____

_____

_____

_____

_____

_____

_____

_____

_____

_____

_____

_____

_____

_____

_____

_____

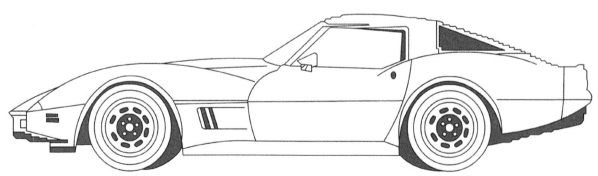

Demonstration Report: Penny Boat

Our Tools

_____   _____

_____   _____

Our Method

What it looked like

It took _____ pennies to sink my boat.

_____

_____

_____

_____

_____

_____

_____

Our Outcome

_____

_____

_____

_____

_____

Our Insight

_____

_____

_____

Digital Machines

_____
_____
_____
_____
_____
_____
_____
_____
_____
_____
_____
_____
_____
_____
_____
_____
_____
_____
_____

Physics for the Grammar Stage

Glossary

106

Acceleration —

_____
_____
_____
_____

Balance —

_____
_____
_____
_____

Battery —

_____
_____
_____
_____

Binary Code —

000010001010
101000101010
101010101010
101010100000
001010101000
001010101001
010101010101

010101010101

Buoyancy —

_____
_____
_____
_____

Capacitor —

_____
_____
_____
_____

Centripetal force —

_____
_____
_____
_____

Circuit —

_____
_____
_____
_____

Conduction —

_____
_____
_____
_____

Conductor —

_____
_____
_____
_____

Convection —

_____
_____
_____
_____

Decibel (dB) —

_____
_____
_____
_____

Density —

_____
_____
_____
_____

Electricity —

_____
_____
_____
_____

Energy —

_____
_____
_____
_____

Energy Chain —

_____
_____
_____
_____

Engine —

_____
_____
_____
_____

Engineer —

_____
_____
_____
_____

Force —

_____
_____
_____
_____

Friction —

_____
_____
_____
_____

Gravity —

_____
_____
_____
_____
_____

Heat —

_____
_____
_____
_____

Inertia —

_____
_____
_____
_____

Infrastructure —

_____
_____
_____
_____

112

Insulator —

_____
_____
_____
_____

Interference —

_____
_____
_____
_____

Lens —

_____
_____
_____
_____

Light —

_____
_____
_____
_____

Load —

Longitudinal Wave —

Lubricant —

Magnet —

114

Mass —

70 kg

_____
_____
_____
_____

Mirror —

_____
_____
_____
_____

Momentum —

_____
_____
_____
_____

Nuclear fission —

_____
_____
_____
_____

Nuclear fusion —

_____
_____
_____
_____

Pole —

_____
_____
_____
_____

Primary colors —

_____
_____
_____
_____

Prototype —

_____
_____
_____
_____

116

Radiation —

_____
_____
_____
_____

Reflection —

Light

Mirror

_____
_____
_____
_____
_____

Refraction —

Light

Lens

_____
_____
_____
_____

Resistor —

_____
_____
_____
_____

Resonate —

Resultant force —

Robot —

Secondary colors —

Shadow—

_____
_____
_____
_____

Simple Machine —

_____
_____
_____
_____

Solar energy —

_____
_____
_____
_____

Sound Wave —

_____
_____
_____
_____

Speed —

_____
_____
_____
_____

Temperature —

_____
_____
_____
_____

Torque —

_____
_____
_____
_____

Transverse Wave —

_____
_____
_____
_____

Weight —

_____
_____
_____
_____

Wind energy —

_____
_____
_____
_____

Work —

_____
_____
_____
_____

Physics for the Grammar Stage

Memory Work

Energy Unit

Energy

Energy is the ability to do work
It comes in different forms - each with their own quirk

Potential energy in an object is stored
Kinetic found in the motion of a skateboard

Light and sound - the energy of waves in motion
Heat is caused by temperature locomotion

Chemical, nuclear - released in reactions
Gravitational - the result of attraction

We use energy in what we do all day long
From holding a ball to hearing a bluebird's song

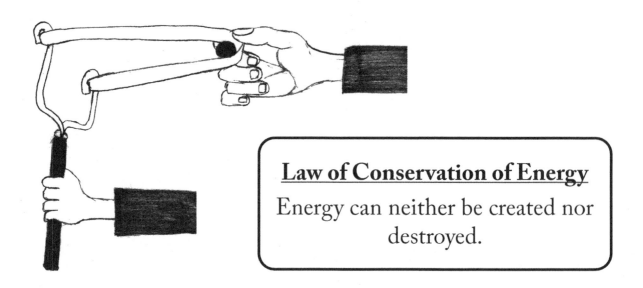

Law of Conservation of Energy
Energy can neither be created nor destroyed.

Light Unit

Light

Light is an electromagnetic wave
Rays that help us to see in a dark cave

All seven colors of visible light
The rainbow does beautifully highlight

Light hits a mirror or shiny object
Bounces back, which we say the rays reflect

Light moves from one substance to another
Rays bend, refraction will trick your brother

A curved transparent surface called a lens
Can focus light rays, on shape it depends

Focused point with concave lens, curved inward
Scattered light with convex lens, curved outward

Colors of the Rainbow (Roy G Biv)

Red
Orange
Yellow
Green
Blue
Indigo
Violet

Sound Unit

Sound

Sound is energy we can hear
Waves that are captured by an ear

Something vibrates and sound waves start
Instruments make sound a fine art

Some sound is soft, some sound is loud
Decibels gauge sound in a crowd

When sound waves meet, changes appear
Waves mix and build or disappear.

Electricity Unit

Electricity

Electricity is charges that move
Particles flowing give power to groove

Conductors allow the current to flow
Insulators stop current, no more go

Circuits show the path of the particles
Wires are the quick shipping articles

Around in a circle, the currents flow
Resistors will cause the currents to slow

Capacitors store and release power
Electronics use to do tasks each hour

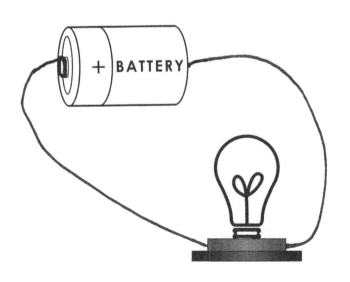

Computers store and use information
Binary code is the bit foundation

Forces Unit

Forces

A push or a pull is known as a force
When an object moves, a force is the source

Balance happens when all the forces still
This time push equals pull and objects chill

Visible forces make a real contact
Invisible ones, like in magnets act

That unseen force pulling you - gravity
The reason you fall in a cavity

Friction is a force that
helps us to grip
It slows us down so that
we do not slip

Look at the forces that
act when boating
You will explain the
physics of floating

Motion Unit

<u>Newton's Three Laws of Motion</u>

1. An object in motion will stay in motion and an object at rest will stay at rest unless they are acted on by an outside force.

2. The greater the force on an object, the greater the change in its motion. The greater the mass of an object, the greater the force needed to change its motion.

3. For every action, there is an equal but opposite reaction.

Engineering Unit

Simple Machines

Simple machines are not complicated
But they help do the hard work dictated

Levers lift big loads through a fixed-point source
Screws turn motion into a driving force

Ramps allow moving up at a fast rate
Pulleys help to lift by spreading out weight

Gears change the speed simply by changing size
Wheels turn around a rod and the load flies

All these modest machines move loads along
They help us to do hard work and look strong

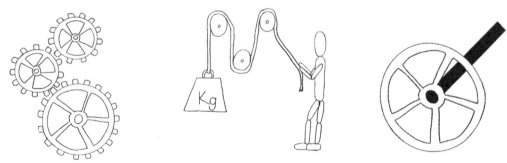

Physics for the Grammar Stage Student Workbook ~ Memory Work

Engineering Unit

__The Engineering Design Process__

The design all begins with an engineer
Who sees a problem or need appear

And questions and researches to be sure
Now, the design goal - no longer obscure

Brainstorming begins, ideas written out
The best one is selected to tryout

The top drawing is built and created
A new prototype is designated

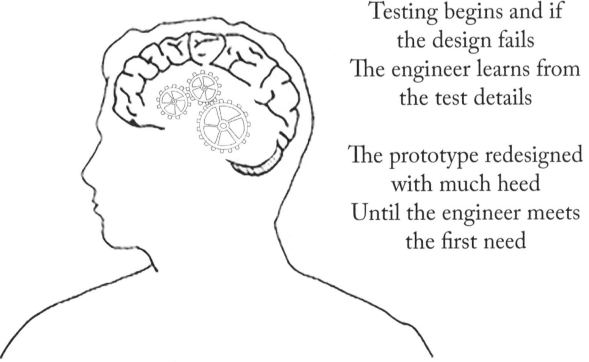

Testing begins and if
the design fails
The engineer learns from
the test details

The prototype redesigned
with much heed
Until the engineer meets
the first need

Physics for the Grammar Stage Student Workbook ~ Memory Work

Physics for the Grammar Stage

Review Sheets

Energy Weekly Review Sheet 1

1. Match the following types of energy.

   Potential Energy   Energy of motion

   Kinetic Energy   Energy that is stored

2. The Law of Conservation of energy says that _____ can

   neither be _____ or _____.

3. **True or False:** An energy chain shows how energy changes forms.

4. What is the most interesting thing you learned this week?

   _____

   _____

   _____

   _____

   _____

134

Energy Weekly Review Sheet 2

1. What is a renewable source of energy?

_____

_____

_____

1. What is a nonrenewable source of energy?

_____

_____

_____

2. **True or False:** Fossil fuels are examples of renewable sources of energy. The wind and sun are examples of nonrenewable sources of energy.

4. What is the most interesting thing you learned this week?

_____

_____

_____

_____

_____

Energy Weekly Review Sheet 3

1. Match the two ways of generating nuclear energy with what happens:

   Nuclear fission   Joining atomic particles to create energy

   Nuclear fusion   Splitting apart atomic particles to create energy

2. **True or False:** Nuclear reactors use controlled fusion reactions.

3. **True or False:** In a nuclear reactor, the energy released heats up water to generate steam that turns a turbine and generates energy.

4. What is the most interesting thing you learned this week?

   _____

   _____

   _____

   _____

   _____

   _____

Energy Weekly Review Sheet 4

1. What is heat?

_____

_____

_____

1. What is temperature?

_____

_____

_____

3. A _____ is an instrument that measures temperature.

4. What is the most interesting thing you learned this week?

_____

_____

_____

_____

_____

_____

Energy Weekly Review Sheet 5

1. Match the type of heat transfer with its definition.

   ___ Convection

   ___ Conduction

   ___ Radiation

   A. The transfer of heat through direct contact.

   B. The transfer of heat through the movement of a liquid and gas.

   C. The transfer of heat through indirect contact.

2. **True or False:** A conductor transfers heat slowly, while an insulator transfers heat quickly.

3. **True or False:** A vacuum is a space completely empty of matter.

4. What is the most interesting thing you learned this week?

Light Weekly Review Sheet 1

1. **True or False:** Light is a form of energy made from an electromagnetic wave.

2. When light passes through a(n) _____ object, it creates a shadow.

      transparent   translucent   opaque

3. Match the object with the way light passes through it.

    _____ Transparent object   A. Light does not pass through.

    _____ Translucent object   B. Light passes completely through.

    _____ Opaque object   C. Light passes partially through.

4. What is the most interesting thing you learned this week?

_____

_____

_____

_____

_____

_____

Light Weekly Review Sheet 2

1. What are the seven colors that make up visible light?

   R _____

   O _____

   Y _____

   G _____

   B _____

   I _____

   V _____

2. **True or False:** Different colors of light have the same wavelength.

4. What is the most interesting thing you learned this week?

_____

_____

- -

- -

- -

- -

Light Weekly Review Sheet 3

1. What happens when light is reflected?

----

2. What happens when light is refracted?

----

3. **True or False:** Iridescence is caused by light rays interfering with each other.

4. What is the most interesting thing you learned this week?

--- Light

Lens

Light Weekly Review Sheet 4

1. **True or False:** A mirror is a curved transparent surface that causes light to bend in a particular way.

2. **True or False:** A lens is a shiny surface that reflects nearly all of the light that hits it.

3. What is the difference between convex and concave lenses?

_____

_____

_____

4. **True or False:** The front part of the eye is a convex converging lens.

5. What is the most interesting thing you learned this week?

_____

_____

_____

_____

_____

_____

_____

Light Weekly Review Sheet 5

1. What have you learned about Thomas Edison this week?

Sound Weekly Review Sheet 1

1. **True or False:** Sound is a mechanical wave that carries energy through a

   medium.

2. Name two things that sound can travel through.

   _____

   _____

3. Name one thing that sound cannot travel through.

   _____

3. **True or False:** An echo of a sound wave cannot be use to determine the

   position of an object.

4. What is the most interesting thing you learned this week?

   _____

   _____

   _____

   _____

   _____

   _____

   _____

Sound Weekly Review Sheet 2

1. What do waves carry?

_____

_____

2. **True or False:** Mechanical waves, such as water waves and sound waves, cause

vibrations in solids, liquids, or gases.

3. Match the type of wave with its description.

____ Longitudinal Wave

A. A wave that vibrates at right angles to the direction of travel.

____ Transverse Wave

B. A wave that vibrates in the same direction as it travels.

4. What is the most interesting thing you learned this week?

Sound Weekly Review Sheet 3

1. **True or False:** A wave never changes speed, direction, or shape when it passes into a different medium (substance).

2. _____ is the effect that happens when two waves meet.

3. Match the type of interference with its description.

_____ Constructive Interference

_____ Destructive Interference

A. The effect that happens when two waves meet and combine to form a larger wave.

B. The effect that happens when two waves meet and cancel each other out.

4. What is the most interesting thing you learned this week?

_____

_____

_____

_____

_____

_____

_____

_____

Sound Weekly Review Sheet 4

1. Match the instrument group with how it works.

_____ Stringed Instruments

_____ Wind Instruments

_____ Percussion Instruments

A. Sound is produced by vibrating strings and then is made fuller and louder by resonating in a soundbox in the instrument.

B. Sound is produced by beating, scraping or shaking the outside and then is amplified by the hollow shape of the instrument.

C. Sound is produced by vibrating a mouthpiece and then is amplified as it travels through the tubes of the instrument.

2. **True or False:** Pitch is the highness or lowness of sound.

3. What is the most interesting thing you learned this week?

Electricity Weekly Review Sheet 1

1. **True or False:** Electricity is the effect created by the movement of charged particles.

2. What is the difference between conductors and insulators?

_____

_____

_____

3. Electricity that is held by material is called _____.

4. What is the most interesting thing you learned this week?

_____

_____

_____

_____

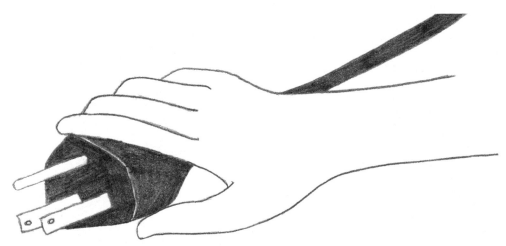

Physics for the Grammar Stage Student Workbook ~ Review Sheets

Electricity Weekly Review Sheet 2

1. An electrical circuit shows _____

_____.

3. Match the type of circuit with its definition.

Series Circuit

A circuit where there is more than one path for the electric current to travel.

Parallel Circuit

A circuit where the components are one after the other.

3. A battery is a store of _____ energy that can be used as

_____ energy. (*Fill in the blanks with the words below.*)

electrical   kinetic   chemical

4. What is the most interesting thing you learned this week?

_ _ _ _ _ _ _ _ _ _ _ _ _ _
_ _ _ _ _ _ _ _ _ _ _ _ _ _
_ _ _ _ _ _ _ _ _ _ _ _ _ _
_ _ _ _ _ _ _ _ _ _ _ _ _ _
_ _ _ _ _ _ _ _ _ _ _ _ _ _
_ _ _ _ _ _ _ _ _ _ _ _ _ _
_ _ _ _ _ _ _ _ _ _ _ _ _ _

Electricity Weekly Review Sheet 3

1. **True or False:** For magnets, like poles attract each other, while unlike poles

   repel.

2. Tell whether the following magnets will attract or repel each other.

   _____ | S | N | | S | N |

   _____ | S | N | | N | S |

3. The area around a magnet that is affected by its magnetic force is called the

   _____ _____.

4. What is the most interesting thing you learned this week?

   _____

   _____

   _____

   _____

   _____

   _____

150

Electricity Weekly Review Sheet 4

1. Match the object with its definition.

_____ Capacitor

_____ Diode

_____ Resistor

_____ Transistor

A. An electrical component that slows the flow of the electric current.

B. An electrical component that stores energy until it is needed.

C. An electrical component that is used as an electrical switch.

D. An electrical component that allows the current to flow through in only one direction.

2. An _____ uses electrical components to control the flow of

_____ in a circuit to do a _____.

3. What is the most interesting thing you learned this week?

_____

_____

_____

_____

_____

_____

Electricity Weekly Review Sheet 5

1. **True or False:** Hardware is the pieces that make up a computer, while software

   is a program, or set of instructions, that tells the computer what to do.

2. What does CPU stand for?

   _____

   _____

3. Computers do their calculations using a series of 1's and 0's, known as

   _____ _____.

4. What is the most interesting thing you learned this week?

   _____

   _____

   _____

   _____

   _____

   _____

Forces Weekly Review Sheet 1

1. What is a force?

_____

_____

2. **True or False:** All forces must be visible.

3. A _____ force is a force that needs two objects to touch.

4. What is the most interesting thing you learned this week?

_____

_____

_____

_____

_____

_____

Forces Weekly Review Sheet 2

1. **True or False:** When the resultant force is equal to zero, an object is balanced.

2. In physics, what does it mean when an object is balanced?

_____

_____

3. **True or False:** When an object is at rest, there are no forces acting on it.

4. What is the most interesting thing you learned this week?

_____

_____

_____

_____

_____

_____

Physics for the Grammar Stage Student Workbook ~ Review Sheets

Forces Weekly Review Sheet 3

1. What is a gravity?

   _____

   _____

2. An object's _____ is the point at which the

   whole weight of an object seems to act.

3. **True or False:** Weight is the amount of matter in an object, while mass is the

   measure of the strength of the pull of gravity on an object.

4. What is the most interesting thing you learned this week?

   _____

   _____

   _____

Physics for the Grammar Stage Student Workbook ~ Review Sheets

Forces Weekly Review Sheet 4

1. What is a friction?

_____

_____

2. **True or False:** A lubricant helps to increase friction.

3. _____ is a type of friction that occurs between air and

an object moving through it.

4 **True or False:** Streamlining a vehicle allows air to flow more smoothly over the

surfaces, reducing the amount of friction.

5. What is the most interesting thing you learned this week?

_____

_____

_____

_____

_____

_____

Forces Weekly Review Sheet 5

1. An object floats because it weighs _____ than the fluid it

   moves out of the way.

2. **True or False:** Archimedes's principle says that the upthrust acting on an object

   is equal to the weight of the fluid that the object displaces.

3. What is a density?

   _____

   _____

4. What is the most interesting thing you learned this week?

   _____

   _____

   _____

   _____

   _____

   _____

Motion Weekly Review Sheet 1

1. (Inertia / Momentum) is the tendency of objects to resist a change in their movement. (Inertia / Momentum) is a measure of an object's tendency to continue moving.

2. **True or False:** An object in motion stays in motion unless acted upon by an outside force.

3. Newton's 2nd law of motion states that the (greater / lesser) the force on an object, the (greater / lesser) the change in motion.

4. Newton's 3rd law of motion states that for every _____, there is an equal but _____.

5. What is the most interesting thing you learned this week?

_____

_____

_____

_____

_____

_____

Physics for the Grammar Stage Student Workbook ~ Review Sheets

Motion Weekly Review Sheet 2

1. Scientists use an object's _____ to describe its motion.

   speed   velocity   acceleration   all of the above

2. **True or False:** Acceleration is a change in an object's speed or direction.

3. What is a speed?

   _____

   _____

4. What is the most interesting thing you learned this week?

   _____

   _____

   _____

   _____

   _____

   _____

Motion Weekly Review Sheet 3

1. **True or False:** Terminal velocity is the maximum velocity reached by a falling object.

2. **True or False:** Objects moving in a circle do not travel in a straight line.

3. What is a centripetal force?

_____

_____

4. What is the most interesting thing you learned this week?

_____

_____

_____

_____

_____

_____

Motion Weekly Review Sheet 4

1. What have you learned about Isaac Newton this week?

_____

_____

_____

_____

_____

_____

_____

_____

Engineering Weekly Review Sheet 1

1. What is a simple machine?

    _____

    _____

2. The _____ is the force of an object's weight that a machine needs to

    overcome.

3. Match the simple machine with what it does.

    _____ Ramp

    _____ Lever

    _____ Screw

    A. It transmits force by turning at a
       fixed point to help lift the load.

    B. It is used to fasten, drill, and move
       loads.

    C. It helps lift a load uphill by
       breaking the work into smaller
       steps.

4. What is the most interesting thing you learned this week?

    _____

    _____

    _____

    _____

    _____

Engineering Weekly Review Sheet 2

1. Match the simple machine with what it does.

_____ Wheel

_____ Gear

_____ Pulley

A. It lets you transfer motion and change speed.

B. It work with an axle to help objects roll.

C. It helps you to lift a weight by spreading it out.

2. What is a work?

_____

_____

3. What is the most interesting thing you learned this week?

_____

_____

_____

_____

_____

_____

Engineering Weekly Review Sheet 3

1. A turbine uses _____ _____ to capture wind or water

   and turn it into _____.

2. **True or False:** A pump pushes around anything that can flow, such as air,

   water or gas.

3. Hydraulics transmit _____ using liquid and pipes.

4. What is the most interesting thing you learned this week?

   _____

   _____

   _____

   _____

   _____

Engineering Weekly Review Sheet 4

1. Put the steps of the engineering design in order.

_____ Test the prototype

_____ Define the design goal

_____ Identify the need or problem

_____ Select the best idea

_____ Do research

_____ Build a prototype

_____ Redesign as needed

_____ Brainstorm for ideas

2. A _____ is a working model that allows engineers to test an idea.

4. What is the most interesting thing you learned this week?

_____

_____

_____

_____

_____

_____

Engineering Weekly Review Sheet 5 Review Sheet

1. Concrete is made from _____, _____, and

   _____.

2. **True or False:** Steel is a mixture of iron and other elements that are heated

   together to form a strong, bendable building material.

3. **True or False:** Plastic is an expensive substitute for aluminum or glass.

4. What is the most interesting thing you learned this week?

   _____

   _____

   _____

   _____

   _____

Engineering Weekly Review Sheet 6

1. _____ are used to cross a river or other obstacle.

2. _____ redirect the downward weight of a structure to prevent collapse.

3. _____ go through obstacles.

4. What is the most interesting thing you learned this week?

_____

_____

_____

_____

_____

_____

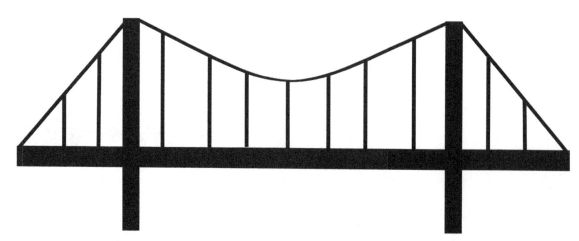

Engineering Weekly Review Sheet 7

1. What is a buoyancy?

_____

_____

2. **True or False:** Submarines do not float.

3. **True or False:** Modern machines, like cars and planes, use fuel-burning

   engines.

4. What is the most interesting thing you learned this week?

_____

_____

_____

_____

_____

_____

Engineering Weekly Review Sheet 8

1. **True or False:** Smartphones are really mini-computers.

2. What is a does GPS stand for?

   _____

   _____

3. A _____ is a machine that does routine tasks on command.

4. What is the most interesting thing you learned this week?

   _____

   _____

   _____

   _____

   _____

   _____

Made in the USA
Las Vegas, NV
17 July 2023

74787758R10096